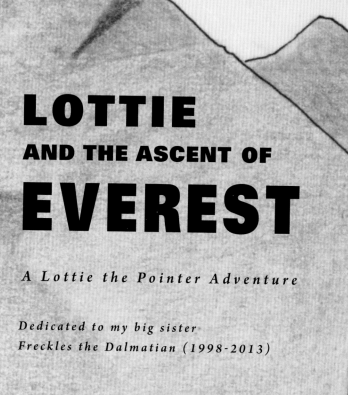

LOTTIE
AND THE ASCENT OF
EVEREST

A Lottie the Pointer Adventure

Dedicated to my big sister
Freckles the Dalmatian (1998-2013)

Written by Rupert Forbes
Illustrated by Bill Talbot

FOREWORD

"I feel honoured to have been asked to write a few words before you read *Lottie's* adventure. It is so important that we encourage young people to explore the outdoors and to learn more about charities and disabilities with compassion and understanding. A perfect opportunity for this to become a reality is by ensuring we invite people who are trying to overcome their challenges so they are included and can enjoy their own adventures with us. When we are faced with difficulties, there should never be barriers to stop us from giving things a go. Overcoming these challenges can be made easier with the support of organisations who understand and the charities *Lottie* is supporting do exactly that.

Charities constantly need funds to deliver vital support and the four charities all make a huge difference to the lives of people whom they have been set up to support. I know this from first hand experience as, after sustaining my spinal cord injury, *Back Up* were integral in rebuilding my confidence, independence and also improving my wheelchair skills. I have participated in a number of physical challenges for charitable causes. This started when I was first in hospital and introduced to the charity.

The charities that will benefit from the sale of *Lottie's* book will help thousands of people of all ages and backgrounds. Thank you very much for buying this book as your donation will go towards helping to improve the lives of others."

With best wishes,

Phil Packer MBE
Founder of The British Inspiration Trust

INTRODUCTION FROM LOTTIE

"Hello Everyone,

I am *Lottie* the English Pointer. I live in Sussex with my family: baby sister *Darcey* (a Large Munsterlander) and two Maine Coon cats, *Audrey* and *George* – and of course our feeder and walker, a Ginger-Haired Person (the GHP as I like to call him). It is quite a responsibility to look after this family, but I like to think I do it pretty well. Oh, I almost forgot, I have three llama friends too, but they live outside (most of the time).

We have plenty of adventures together and a couple of years ago I had the idea of helping some very worthy charities by challenging myself, with a little help from the GHP, to climb as high as Mount Everest, the world's highest mountain. The charities were *Back Up*, the *Down's Syndrome Association*, *Hospice in the Weald* and *Motor Neurone Disease Association*. There is information about each of them and the excellent work they do at the end of this book (as well as details of all the mountains we climbed).

While I was undertaking my challenge, I kept a blog so my kind supporters could follow my progress. I have now written this book to share my adventures during the challenge more widely and to raise further funds for the charities. This is the story of those adventures and I hope you enjoy it as much as I did the challenge itself!"

Hugs and licks,

Lottie x

We all dream. The GHP tells me he dreams of the highest mountains.

The cats are, I assume, only fixated with computers
(they keep telling me about their latest mouse dreams);
while Darcey I know just dreams of being like me
one day. Now I dream of mountains too - mountains
of my favourite bone-shaped dog treats, special
Mountain Morsels (MMs).

The highest mountain the GHP dreams of is Mount Everest, but they won't let me climb Everest - some issue with my passport photo. We therefore decide to climb a series of mountains that together are even higher than Everest. The total height will exceed 30,000 paws - feet to you - all to raise money for those wonderful charities.

Any venture into the mountains needs proper research and planning and I regularly help the GHP with his online digging (in fact any digging) to ensure he remembers all the important things.

Being able to pack light and efficiently is very important when going into the mountains. Safety comes first as you never know what the weather will throw at you.

You have to bear in mind that you (or your GHP) will be carrying everything. Make sure that you neither pack anything unnecessary nor forget anything critical.

Eating properly when you are in the mountains is something else that I never forget. So I make sure I have plenty of healthy food to keep up my strength at all times.

Also remember to check everything one last time before you leave so you don't take anything you don't really need (George...get off the car roof please).

Eating properly before you start your climbing day is equally important. For the first leg of our adventure we are joined by the GHP's sisters. He has lots of them, all of whom have ginger hair... and if they leave their toast uneaten then why shouldn't I eat it? We are going to climb Ben Lomond, a Munro (more about this later).

First we must go on a boat ride across the loch to the start of the walk. I picture myself in the prow of the boat just like Kate Winslett in Titanic... Note to 'self - check there are no icebergs on the loch before I get on board.

The GHP tells me that to get on the boat we have to "embark". Well I do my best at this; mainly em barking at the group of ducks near the dock. Once on the boat, the passengers embark on songs about high and low roads, which makes no sense when we are in the middle of a loch. Getting off a boat is "disembarking", so I get off quietly at the other side of the loch.

BEN LOMOND
HT 3196 PAWS

The next step in our mountain climb is to check the map;
I can safely leave this to the GHP and his sisters because the
path up this particular mountain is as wide as a motorway.
I pass the time meeting another group of large and
ginger-haired creatures, Highland Cows... or maybe the
GHP has more sisters than he has told me about after all...

It is very important in the mountains that a leader takes the lead. I have plenty of leads so it is only right that I lead the GHP and his sisters up the very complex path to the summit. I let them do a spot of navigating, as being an English Pointer I'm not a fully trained guide dog (I am not a Labrador after all!). The sisters keep talking about the view – though to me the inside of one misty cloud is pretty much the same as the inside of another. Now, getting to the top of a mountain is only half the challenge...

BEN LO

The most important half is to get back down safely. If you can get down more quickly than the rest of your group there will be time to enjoy an ice cream while waiting for the boat ride home, even if it is a bit cold on the tongue. So we have a Munro, an ice cream and over 3,000 paws in the bag - that is one tenth of the target already.

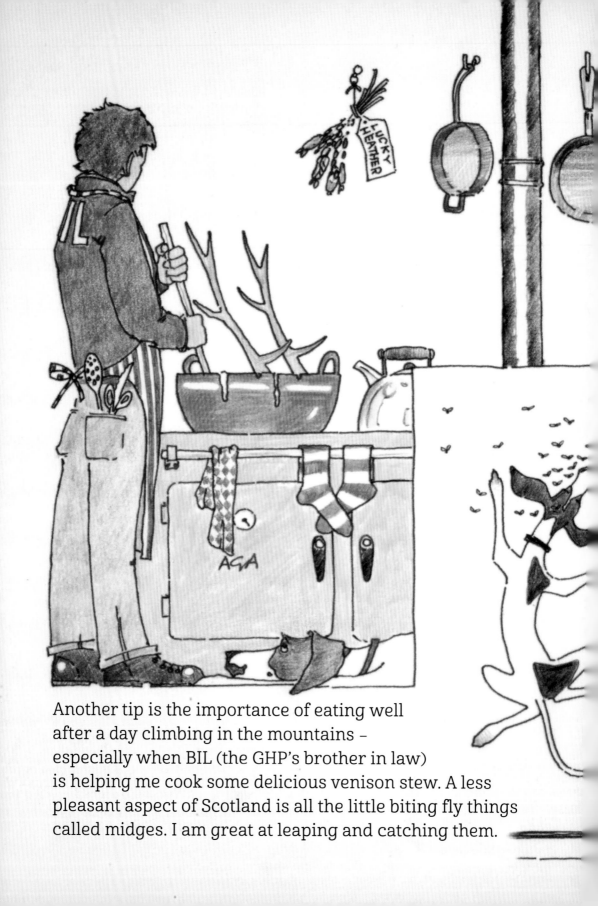

Another tip is the importance of eating well
after a day climbing in the mountains –
especially when BIL (the GHP's brother in law)
is helping me cook some delicious venison stew. A less
pleasant aspect of Scotland is all the little biting fly things
called midges. I am great at leaping and catching them.

I'm also great at leaping and catching pieces of venison before they fall into the cooking pot. I can't understand why I have now been barred from the kitchen and I dutifully turn my attention to updating my blog so people can see how I am getting on with the challenge.

MUNRO   BEINN   GRAHA

Now I am a smart Pointer, especially when my coat has been brushed, but I do get my paws a bit muddled when it comes to names for mountains in Scotland.

A spot of online research (and as my coat shows, I do like spots) reveals that there are Munros (over 3,000 paws), Corbetts (over 2,500 paws, though the only Corbett I know is called Ronnie and very short, so this strikes me as odd) and Grahams (over 2,000 paws). Almost all mountains in Scotland seem to be called Beinn or Ben. Well that clears that up...not.

Next up is a big three-mountain day
including two Munros and three Bens
(still confused? – I am), finishing up
on top of the Cobbler, one of the most
popular mountains in Southern Scotland.

The approach to Ben Narnain is quite rocky near the top in Spearhead Gulley, so we ditch anything unnecessary; in this case the GHP's sisters.

I demonstrate my mountain skills at leading and belaying to help the GHP along the way. This is where good harness work is essential – it may look like tugging on the lead, but it is certainly not (take note Darcey).

I guide the GHP down the far side and on up Ben Ime. With a Mountain Morsel or two on each summit to keep up my strength, it is not long before I scent out the sisters ambling up the easy route to the top of the Cobbler (also called Ben Arthur or Beinn Artur – still confused...?).

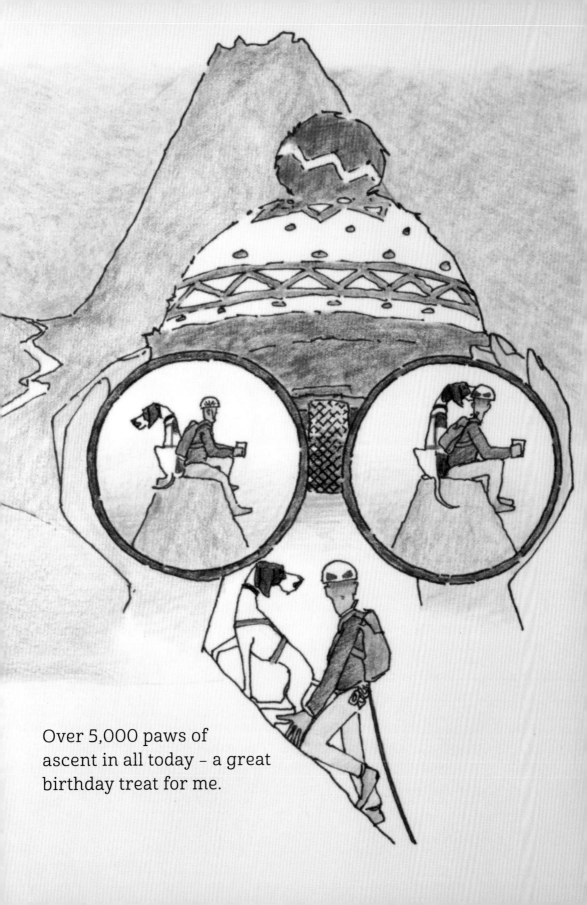

Over 5,000 paws of
ascent in all today – a great
birthday treat for me.

The view from the top of Ben Narnain and Ben Ime earlier in the day had been the same as that from Ben Lomond, but even through the mist I can see that the Cobbler is different. To reach the very top you have to do something called "threading the needle" – but have you ever tried threading a needle with paws?

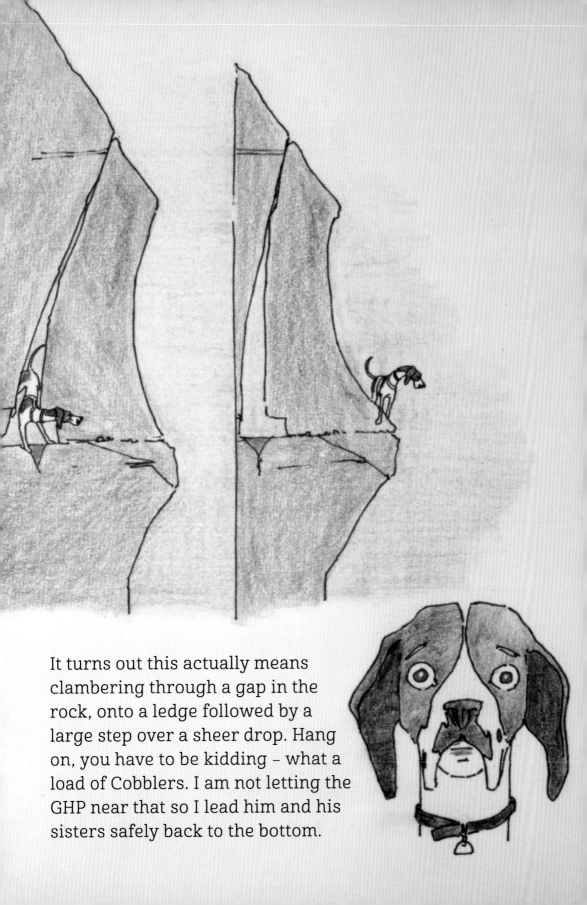

It turns out this actually means clambering through a gap in the rock, onto a ledge followed by a large step over a sheer drop. Hang on, you have to be kidding – what a load of Cobblers. I am not letting the GHP near that so I lead him and his sisters safely back to the bottom.

After all these paws in Scotland, we are back home to prepare for the next leg of the challenge. The GHP says we are off to see some Whales and I am likely to be snowed-on. We will see lots of white woolly things too (I think he means sheep, though the last time I tried to count them I fell asleep). I know that Whales are big, but are they really over 3,000 paws high? Perhaps the GHP is starting to suffer altitude sickness. Darcey isn't helping at all.

Now any challenge has to push you to your limits, but I have to say all my research into Whales, woolly white things and being snowed-on is giving me nightmares.

To cheer myself up, I take a break in my planning to attend to a few media responsibilities including an interview on local radio. As you would expect I get the important points across (I am very good at pointing even if I say so myself) about my challenge and the charities I am supporting. My family at home is very impressed with my achievements.

I am not sure why we are setting off in the dark to get snowed-on. On the Miners Track, we meet a fierce mountain goat who hates early mornings as much as I do, but I keep the GHP safe with my head torch. I am admiring the sunrise when we hit mist and a howling gale on the summit ridge (are we back in Scotland?). We go up Carnedd Ugain, and then on to the top of Snowdon - the UK's highest mountain outside Scotland - named, I learn, after the train station on the summit. There are no Whales in sight.

There are lots of sheep but not another soul. To be fair, at 8 in the morning everyone in their right mind should still be in bed. It's a good thing I booked a train ticket for a relaxing journey back down to my comfy bed.

Seems we are not taking the train down after all, but walking. We pass some other people – finally - who are certainly not properly dressed for mist or howling gales. No wonder the mountain rescue service is so busy. I may have fun in the mountains, but I respect them and that means being properly prepared and equipped.

Nor are we stopping at the car – but heading for yet another mountain, Tryfan. At the top we reach a pair of rock pedestals called Adam and Eve. The GHP says brave people can jump between them! With the wind getting ever stronger, and a mountain rescue helicopter overhead, I let the GHP have a warming cup of tea before guiding him safely back down after another day of almost 5,000 paws.

Planning the final leg of the challenge is proving difficult. Darcey is still not helping, while at the same time all of the UK's mountains have been covered with snow for several months now. The GHP checks out the forecast from our local weather presenter (one of them doesn't seem to know their 'c's from their 'k's, so what chance of knowing the klimatic konditions)? I therefore look at sensible alternatives.

Finally it seems that we will be heading back to Scotland to complete the challenge. With a risk of isolated snow patches up high, it is time to check our use of crampons (you put them on your paws to help grip in snow and ice). It is an important part of walking in the mountains to be familiar with all your equipment before you actually need it and we want to be safe and properly prepared.

After the disappointment on Snowdon, I am at last
going to travel on a train – the Caledonian Sleeper from
London to Fort William (another confusing place name –
was there a fight with BIL?).

CALEDONIAN SLEEPER

I let the GHP have the top bunk, though I am not sure why
I have to share my bacon roll with him when we awake
in Scotland the following morning - he can have the cup
of tea. Looking out of the window, I realise how beautiful
mountains are when you can actually see them.

Today I get the chance to climb a mountain in Scotland that is not named Ben. This one is Carn Mor Dearg, another Munro (and over 4,000 paws - my highest to-date), though it is right next to a Ben (Ben Nevis, the UK's highest mountain).

With beautiful spring weather it is a perfect day in the mountains. I spend a lot of the ascent racing around and pointing out all the grouse to the GHP – we Pointer girls are good at multi-tasking.

Three quarters of the way up, we pass the height of Mount Everest. By the time we reach the summit, we have climbed more than 30,000 paws. I have become a Pointer truly on top of the world (and not just because I have a view for once). I have successfully completed my challenge.

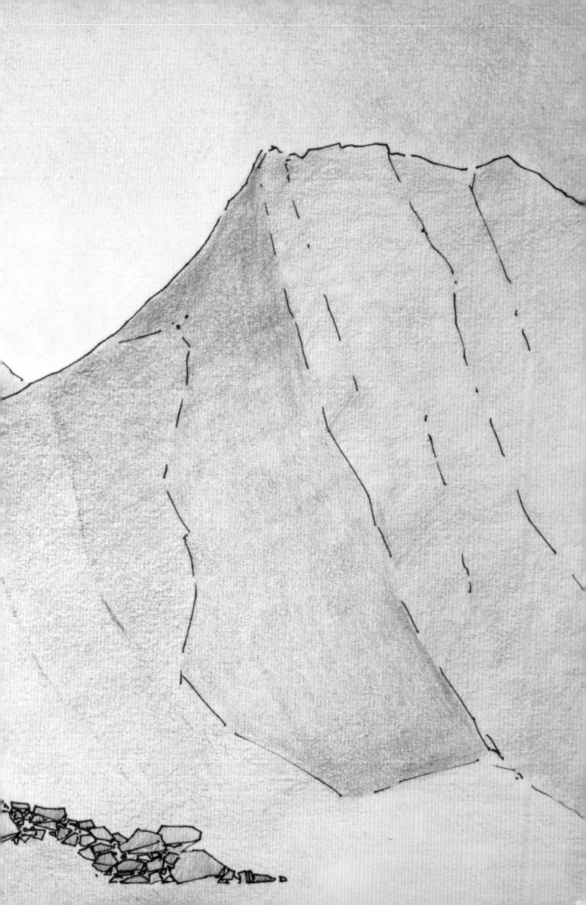

Lottie the Pointer has successfully climbed higher than Mount Everest and she makes her way down to take the sleeper train home and dream of her next adventure. *Lottie* will return in...

Lottie has written and produced this book in support of the following charities:

-    *Back Up*
-    *Down's Syndrome Association*
-    *Hospice in the Weald*
-    *Motor Neurone Disease Association*

All of the profits raised through the sale of this edition of the book will be donated to the above four charities equally.

ACKNOWLEDGEMENTS

Even an adept English Pointer like myself needs help when it comes to producing a book and I would like to give huge thanks to the following – as well as everyone else who has assisted or contributed to the process in any way.

Bill Talbot - for capturing my best side so well in his illustrations. Bill is a talented artist who has not had to illustrate any of my books before – probably as this is my first one. He is a figurative artist whose life drawings are edgy collaborations of light, movement and tension and whose website includes a review stating that he loves, above all, the female body in its prime. It was not hard therefore for me to decide that this was the right person to depict both my elegance and my edgy and tension filled adventures (though he could be more generous with the biscuits when he comes round).
w. billtalbot.com

Phil Packer - for agreeing to write a very kind foreword to the book – most particularly with the underlying theme of inspiration which I try to bring to all that I do - even if at times Darcey seems more focused on bringing exasperation.
w. britishinspirationtrust.org.uk

Alastair Harlow - for his help with the graphic-side production of this book and the design of my website, as well as leaving his sunglasses here for me to model.
w. cosystudios.com

Yeomans – for their work to print and promote this book. Yeomans marketing is an eclectic band of creative thinkers, strategic marketers, fundraising specialists, designers, innovators and project managers (their words not mine, though sounds a lot like me). They work in the not for profit and charity sector and care passionately about making a difference to both their direct clients and to the individuals whom those charities support and serve.
w. yeomansmarketing.co.uk

Kaddy Lee-Preston – for her consistent weather forecasting (rain, rain, snow, rain) and for agreeing to appear with me in the book.
w. kaddyblog.com

Charlie Allan and Saor Patrol – for their musical inspiration and support for my venture. For those of you who don't know them and, aside from their unique brand of music, they often appear as scary people in films (Charlie was the German chieftain in the opening scene of Gladiator) while supporting social and educational projects through the Clanranald Trust and their Duncarron medieval fort in Scotland.
w. clanranald.org

And last but not least:

The GHP and my Mistress – for feeding me and walking me and letting me use the home computer to write this book. They also assure me they have done a full spelling and grandma check (at least that is what I think they said).

w. backuptrust.org

**Registered Charity No.
1072216 and SCO40577**

"We are very proud to support *Lottie's* book who so ably supported *Back Up* by getting to the top of Snowdon in 2013, raising considerable funds to ensure more people affected by spinal cord injury received the help they needed."

Back Up is a national charity that transforms the lives of people affected by spinal cord injury.

Our vision is:

A world where people with spinal cord injury can realise their full potential.

Our purpose is to:

- Inspire people affected by spinal cord injury to transform their lives.
- Challenge perceptions of disability.
- Deliver services that build confidence and independence and offer a supportive network.

Back Up has helped thousands of people of all ages and backgrounds rebuild their confidence and independence following a devastating spinal cord injury. Our wheelchair skills training, mentoring service and rehabilitative activity courses are all run by people who have a spinal cord injury themselves. We also support people to overcome the challenges of returning to work or school. We understand that a spinal cord injury can be devastating, but believe it should not prevent anyone from fulfilling their potential. Our services open people's eyes and inspire them to look forward to a more positive future.

"It was great when *Lottie* went on local radio, together with one of the children we help and his mother, to promote her Everest challenge - thank you now *Lottie* for continuing to support us through this book."

Who we are:

The *Down's Syndrome Association* is the only charity in the UK dealing with all aspects of Down's syndrome. Our aim is to help people with Down's syndrome live full and rewarding lives.

What we do:

All our services are accessible to everyone regardless of where they live; we have regional offices in England, Wales and Northern Ireland as well as a network of affiliated support groups across the country.

We increase awareness and understanding of the condition through training, publications and resources, our website, social media and the Information helpline. We provide training on all aspects of enhancing the life experiences of children & adults with Down's syndrome. Our training for professionals, family and carers covers child development, speech & language development, education and positive ageing.

Our assessment service for children can focus on any issue associated with a child's development and education, including progress, teaching methods, social development and behaviour. A parallel service is available for adults.

The *Down's Syndrome Association* also runs Support Programmes:

DSActive provides children and young adults with Down's syndrome an opportunity to get involved in sports.
w. dsactive.org

WorkFit is an employment initiative designed to bridge the gap between employers and employees with Down's syndrome.
w. dsworkfit.org.uk

w. hospiceintheweald.org.uk

Registered Charity No.
280276

"*Lottie* is very talented and has a great sense of humor... but don't tell her, it'll just go to her head. Please give her a big hug and a doggy treat from us to thank her."

Hospice in the Weald is the leading palliative care provider for the communities of West Kent and northern East Sussex. We are not part of the NHS but are a local charity rooted in the community we serve and offer varied but integrated services for people with terminal illnesses, their carers and families.

Hospice in the Weald provides specialist palliative care to individuals with terminal or life-limiting illness. This care extends beyond the individual to those important to them, for example, their families, friends and carers. Our care aims to incorporate the individual's physical, psychological, social, religious/spiritual and cultural needs. *Hospice in the Weald*, therefore, provides a multi-professional service to those in need in our community.

Our core values are:

- To put patients first.
- To support patients, carers, and their families.
- To deliver the most effective specialist palliative care we can.
- To respect and value the contribution of all *Hospice in the Weald* staff, trustees and volunteers.
- To be open, honest and transparent in all that we do.
- To make best possible use of funds and to ensure value for money.

"Without amazing supporters like *Lottie* we simply would not be able to deliver our mission and take steps toward our vision of a world free from MND. We rely on voluntary donations and would like to take this opportunity to thank *Lottie* (and her fans) for such valuable support."

The *MND Association* was founded in 1979 and we are the only national charity in England, Wales and Northern Ireland focused on MND care, research and campaigning.

The *MND Association's* mission:

- We improve care and support for people with MND, their families and carers.
- We fund and promote research that leads to new understanding and treatments, and brings us closer to a cure for MND.
- We campaign and raise awareness so the needs of people with MND and everyone who cares for them are recognised and addressed by wider society.

What is MND?

- MND is a fatal, rapidly progressive disease that affects the brain and spinal cord.
- It attacks the nerves that control movement; people can still think and feel, but their muscles refuse to work.
- It can leave people locked in a failing body, unable to move, talk and eventually breathe.
- It affects people from all communities.
- It kills five people every day in the UK, half within 14 months of diagnosis.
- It affects up to 5,000 adults in the UK at any one time.
- It has no cure.

LOTTIE'S EVEREST CHALLENGE LOG

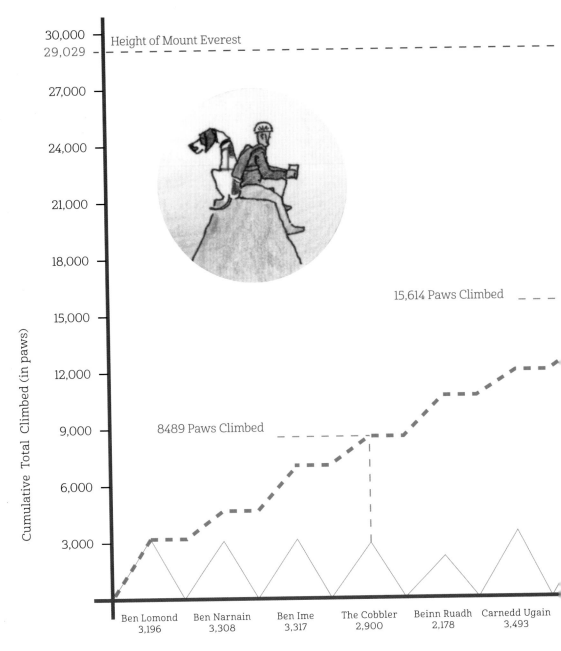

Height of Mount Everest

30,000
29,029

27,000

24,000

21,000

18,000

15,000

15,614 Paws Climbed

12,000

Cumulative Total Climbed (in paws)

9,000

8489 Paws Climbed

6,000

3,000

Ben Lomond	Ben Narnain	Ben Ime	The Cobbler	Beinn Ruadh	Carnedd Ugain
3,196	3,308	3,317	2,900	2,178	3,493

Individual Mountain Heights (in paws)

The graph reflects the cumulative/total paws actually climbed during the challenge.
The heights of individual mountains are listed for interest, but only the actual height/part
of the mountain climbed counted towards the challenge total.

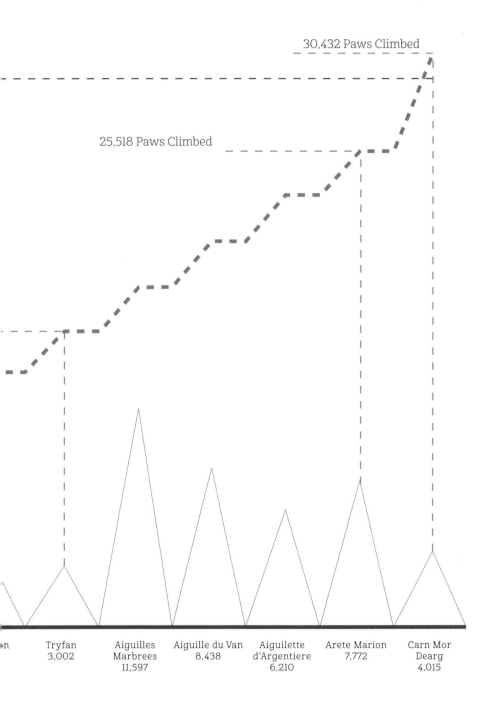

30,432 Paws Climbed

25,518 Paws Climbed

n   Tryfan   Aiguilles   Aiguille du Van   Aiguilette   Arete Marion   Carn Mor
     3,002   Marbrees   8,438   d'Argentiere   7,772   Dearg
                 11,597   6,210   4,015

The GHP had to climb some additional peaks in France (with Lottie at base camp) which are included in the graph but not described in the book. This was for him to catch up with the height climbed by Lottie on other days as he is much slower than her and never climbs as far.